BETTER DAY BOOKS

SCHIFFER PUBLISHING

Better Day Books
P.O. Box 21462
York, PA 17402
Phone: 717-487-5523
Email: hello@betterdaybooks.com
www.betterdaybooks.com
@better_day_books

Schiffer Publishing
4880 Lower Valley Road
Atglen, PA 19310
Phone: 610-593-1777
Fax: 610-593-2002
Email: info@schifferbooks.com
www.schifferbooks.com

This title is available for promotional or commercial use,
including special editions. Contact info@schifferbooks.com
for more information.

Beautiful World

Coloring Book

CAR PINTOS

BETTER DAY BOOKS

HAPPY · CREATIVE · CURATED

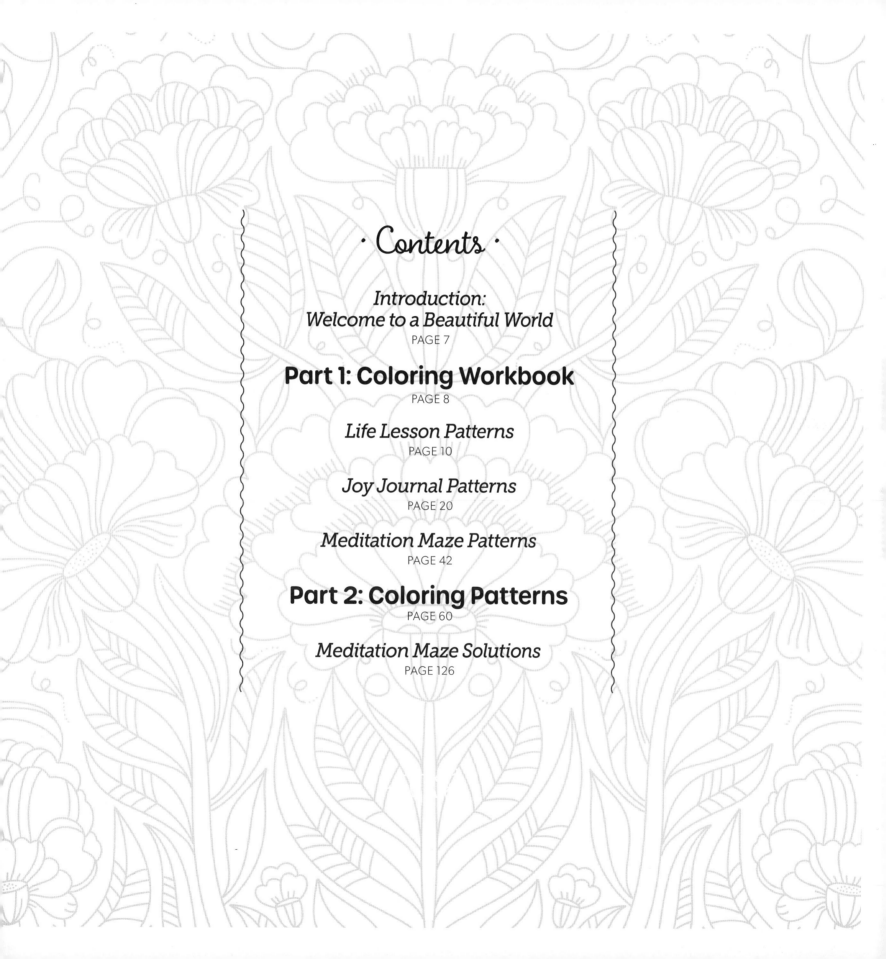

· Contents ·

Welcome to a Beautiful World

I hope the coloring patterns in this book will bring you the same feeling of contentment, relaxation, and joy that they bring me.

When I was a child living in Argentina, I took art and drawing lessons. I played, painted, and observed. I became friends with this world immediately. I still remember how I learned to discover beautiful colors through the magic of watercolor. Today, my family and I live in Mar Chiquita, Buenos Aires (a World Biosphere Reserve). We create among the butterflies, dunes, fish, flamingos, flowers, hummingbirds, and trees. We are wrapped in nature, and I am inspired by everything around me. The illustrations in this book are my stories. They are lush with detail because nature, infinite in its beauty, calls me to draw that way.

Coloring is a wonderful way to escape the stresses of everyday life and allow your mind to dream, wonder, and relax. To heighten this experience, I have included journal pages to accompany many of the patterns. Ponder each journal entry as you color your way through the book. Record your thoughts in the spaces provided and reflect back on your writing later. It is my wish that this book not only will provide you with a creative outlet but will also inspire you to see and engage meaningfully with the beautiful world around you.

I believe life is the way we paint it—and I choose to fill mine with color.

Thank you for joining me on this coloring adventure!

Car Pintos

Part 1

COLORING WORKBOOK

Make a Wish

Remind yourself daily of the dreams and goals you are working toward. You can help yourself manifest those dreams by not losing sight of them. Speak affirmations to yourself like "I am capable of achieving what I set out to do" and "I have the power to change my life." These things are true for everyone!

What are my dreams and goals?

....

....

....

....

....

....

....

What affirmations speak to me?

....

....

....

....

....

....

....

Seek the Sun

Just like sunflowers will grow toward the sun, so too must you make positivity a priority. You will have the energy to work hard toward your goals only if you surround yourself with people who lift you up and an environment that energizes you rather than drains you. Soak in the sunlight and turn it into something beautiful!

What are some positive things I can surround myself with?

....

....

....

....

....

....

....

....

Who are some positive people I can seek out?

....

....

....

....

....

....

....

....

Bloom in Adversity

No goal, dream, or, indeed, life, is without its setbacks and hard times. But flowers don't grow without any rainy days! Every time you are faced with a challenge or thrown a curve ball, it is an opportunity to rise to the occasion and learn something valuable. So next time it rains, don't bemoan the weather—take it in and come out stronger.

What challenges have I overcome lately?

....

....

....

....

....

....

....

What have I learned lately?

....

....

....

....

....

....

....

· *Life Lesson* ·

Celebrate Uniqueness

No matter the size or style of your goals, no matter the colors of petals, no matter if you achieve everything in record time or are still on the journey, you should stand tall in your unique authenticity. Your beauty is your own; celebrate the diversity that surrounds you and your own special place in the world.

What makes me special and unique?

....

....

....

....

....

....

....

....

What are my favorite things about myself?

....

....

....

....

....

....

....

....

· Joy Journal ·

Keep Going

Keep going, keep growing.
There is always something new to experience!

Use the spaces below to reflect on what you want to accomplish in the future.

Goals for This Week

....

....

....

....

Goals for This Month

....

....

....

....

Goals for This Year

....

....

....

Trust the Process

Not every step in your personal journey is fun— but they're all important.

Use the spaces below to think back on recent events.

What is something that was difficult, but I am glad happened?

....

....

....

....

....

What is something I learned during a recent setback?

....

....

....

....

....

· Joy Journal ·

Enjoy the Journey

Life is full of moments, large and small, that all contribute to our story.

Use the spaces below to highlight positive moments that stand out in your recent memory.

Something Tiny That Brought Me Joy

....

....

....

Something Big That Made Me Happy

....

....

....

Something That Made Me Laugh Out Loud

....

....

....

Something That Made Me Feel Connected to the Universe

....

....

....

· Joy Journal ·

Live in the Moment

You're never in the past or the future—
you are only ever here and now.

Use the spaces below to focus on this very moment.

What am I seeing?

....
....
....

What am I hearing?

....
....
....

What am I feeling?

....
....
....

What am I smelling or tasting?

....
....
....

· Joy Journal ·

Believe in Yourself

Only you control your body and mind; only you control your life.

Use the spaces below to list some of things that fill you with confidence.

My Strengths

....

....

....

....

My Skills

....

....

....

....

My Accomplishments

....

....

....

What People Seek Me Out For

....

....

....

Follow Your Heart

Your head may be smart,
but sometimes the heart knows best.

Use the spaces below to reflect on how your heart guides you.

When have I followed my heart in the past?

....

....

....

....

How can I follow my heart in the future?

....

....

....

....

How does it feel when my heart is fulfilled?

....

....

....

· Joy Journal ·

You Are Not Your Thoughts

Thoughts come and go; it is actions that matter most.

Use the spaces below to examine how thoughts serve you or hold you back.

What scenarios bring up negative thoughts?

....

....

....

....

What scenarios bring up positive thoughts?

....

....

....

....

How often am I plagued by anxious or intrusive thoughts?

....

....

....

What can I do to acknowledge negative thoughts, but then let them go?

....

....

....

you are not your thoughts

Accept This Moment as It Is

You cannot change what is happening, but you can accept it and act to change what happens next.

In the space below, write a sentence or paragraph about accepting the moment.

I acknowledge this moment and . . .

....

....

....

....

....

....

....

· Joy Journal ·

Be Aware

What is going on in the world outside your own head?

Get up and go outside! Use the spaces below to write about what is happening out there.

Where have I gone? Describe it.

....

....

....

....

What is different here from where I was?

....

....

....

....

What am I seeing and hearing?

....

....

....

....

Who is out here living their own lives?

....

....

....

....

Chase Your Dreams

Your dreams will not come to you. You have to pursue them!

Use the space below to list some concrete steps toward achieving a dream.

Concrete Steps or Tasks I Can Take to Achieve My Dreams

· Meditation Maze ·

COMFORT

This moth would like to hide among the flowers, where it is camouflaged. Think about places and people where you feel safe and comfortable as you help it find its way.

ABUNDANCE

The berry bush is bursting with sweet treats!
As you guide the bird to its dinner, reflect on ways
in which your life is overflowing with good things.

CURIOSITY

What do you wonder about the world? Let your mind fill
with questions—but no pressure to immediately answer them!—
as you guide the curious jellyfish to the conch shell.

PATIENCE

This butterfly is contending with a windy day on its way to a flower, but it knows it will get there eventually. Try to calm your mind and be patient as you slowly trace the path.

CONNECTION

The planet winds its way around the sun, linked in an eternal dance. As you trace a path between the two, think about all the ways you are connected to the earth and your loved ones.

· Meditation Maze ·

GRATITUDE

This bird is about to enjoy a delicious fruit—if you can guide
it there! What do you love in life that you are thankful for?

· *Meditation Maze* ·

SHARING

There is plenty of room in the thicket for this fox and all
the beetles and bugs. Lead the fox to the leafy flowers while
you think about how good it feels to live in a world
where we share with others.

FRIENDSHIP

Even the most unlikely pair—like this flamingo and fish—can become friends. As you guide the pair to one another, feel the warmth in your soul that comes from your own dear friends.

BRAVERY

The delicate butterfly strikes out into the world despite knowing the risks life presents. It will seek out its flower regardless. Help it along its journey as you reflect on what it means to be brave.

Part 2
COLORING PATTERNS

The End

· Meditation Maze Solutions ·

COMFORT
page 43

ABUNDANCE
page 45

CURIOSITY
page 47

PATIENCE
page 49

CONNECTION
page 51

GRATITUDE
page 53

SHARING
page 55

FRIENDSHIP
page 57

BRAVERY
page 59

BETTER DAY BOOKS

HAPPY · CREATIVE · CURATED

Business is personal at Better Day Books. We were founded on the belief that all people are creative and that making things by hand is inherently good for us. It's important to us that you know how much we appreciate your support. The book you are holding in your hands was crafted with the artistic passion of the author and brought to life by a team of wildly enthusiastic creatives who believed it could inspire you. If it did, please drop us a line and let us know about it. Connect with us on Instagram, post a photo of your art, and let us know what other creative pursuits you are interested in learning about. It all matters to us. You're kind of a big deal.

it's a good day to have a better day!

www.betterdaybooks.com
⊙ better_day_books